MAX

THE MACMILLAN COMPANY
NEW YORK · CHICAGO
DALLAS · ATLANTA · SAN FRANCISCO
LONDON · MANILA

**THE MACMILLAN COMPANY
OF CANADA, LIMITED**
TORONTO

MAX

by GIOVANNETTI

THE MACMILLAN COMPANY - NEW YORK - 1957

TO NINI WITH LOVE

1

2

3

4

5

6

ABOUT MAX

When questioned closely about details concerning his parentage, early environmental influences, adolescent trauma, and other such data so necessary to an understanding of genius, Max tends to shuffle his feet and look unseeingly over your shoulder. He has, on occasion, shown a few intimate friends a miniature of his grandfather, Captain Rufus, a disreputable-looking old salt with a peg leg who engaged in dubious commercial ventures on various unregistered ships under vague flags, mainly in the South Pacific. It is said that he once left Singapore under a cloud, an almost impossible feat.

The reasons for Max's reluctance to discuss his past are obscure. He is certainly not shy. Exhibitionism, indeed, is one of his chronic shortcomings, along with vanity, stubbornness, gluttony, impetuosity, and an almost disastrous degree of optimistic self-confidence. One wonders, in view of these grave failings, how this small wayward creature can command such indulgent and universal affection. In some circles, an anti-Max sentiment is tantamount to an admission of treason, diabolism, and lack of sportsmanship.

7

8

9

I have asked several leaders in various fields to explain Max's extraordinary popularity. *"Zeitgeist* in reverse," a noted philosopher told me. He meant, I think, that one would never find Max looking like this:

An eminent psychiatrist spoke of "compulsive manic patterns superimposed upon dormant hysterical impulses: altogether abnormally normal." A Hollywood producer waved his cigar excitedly and said, "He is simply tremendous, completely gigantic, absolutely *four*-D!" A well known poet put it this way: "The naked bulb in the skull/Burns shards of glitter/And papier-mâché blooms where he walks/Like Etruscan trellises." A certain United States Senator remarked confidentially to the nation, "We have nothing definite on him in our files, and if you will allow me to say so, I find this in itself a highly suspicious circumstance."

None of these comments quite succeeds in pin-pointing the elusive quality that is Max. Elf, demon, child, artist, impresario, athlete, *homme du monde* — he is all of these, and yet, and yet . . . is he any more complex than the simple gift of laughter? Or any less?

JOHN MEREDITH

MAX

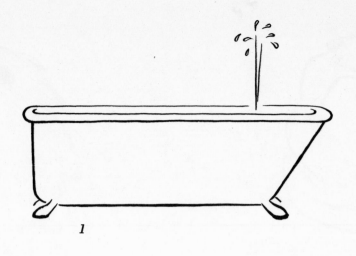

1

2

3

4

5

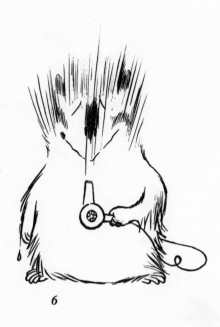

6

7

8

3

2

1

4

5

6

3

2

1

4

5

6

7

1

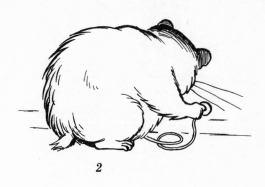

2

3

4

5

6

7

8

1

2

3

4

5

6

7

8

9

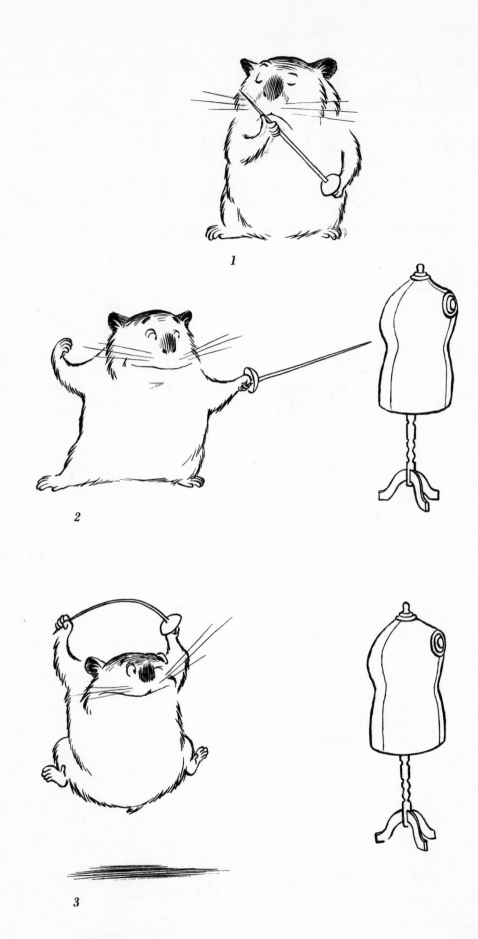

1

2

3

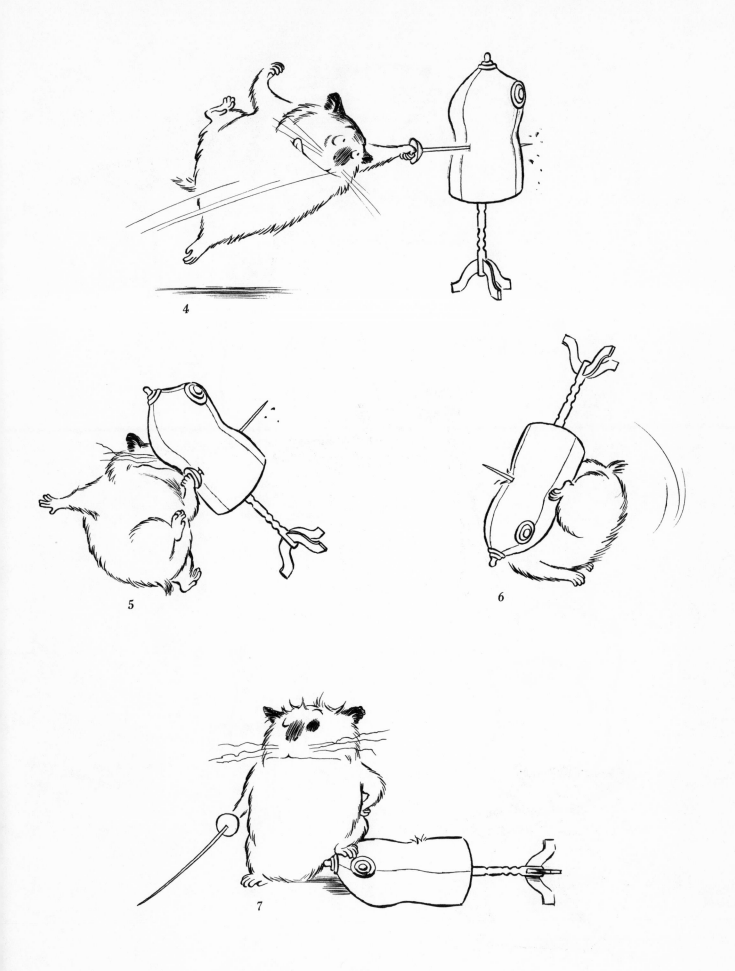

4

5

6

7

3

2

1

4

5

6

1

2

3

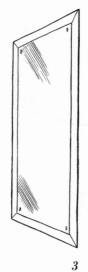

4

5

6

7

8

1

2

3

4

5

1

2

4

3

5

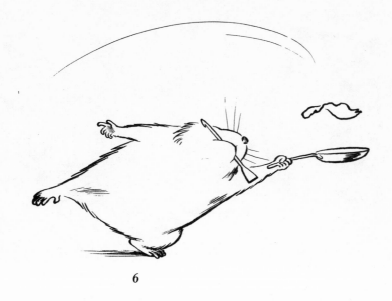

6

7

8

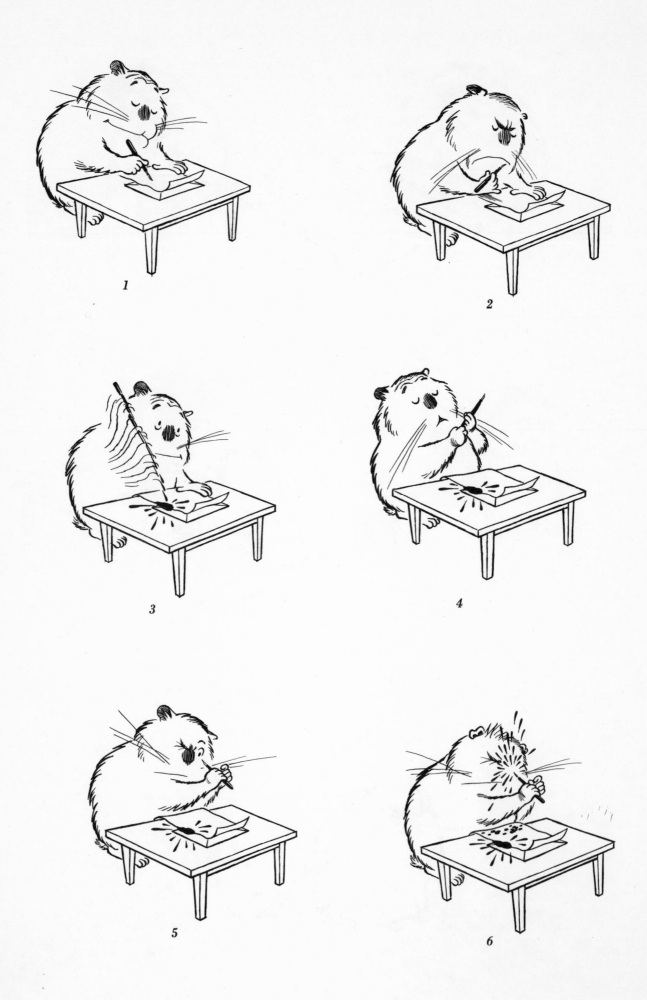

1

2

3

4

5

6

7

1

2

3

4

5

6

7

8

9

10

1

2

3

4

5

6

3

2

1

4

5

6

7

1

2

3

4

5

6

7

8

5

4

6

2

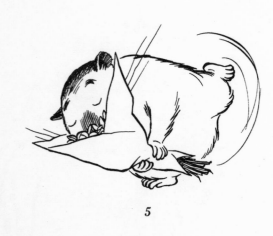

1

3

7

8

9

10

1

2

3

4

5

6

7

8

1

2

3

4

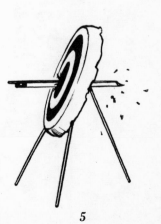

5

4

5

6

7 *forty-nine*

1

2

3

4

5

6

7

8

5

6

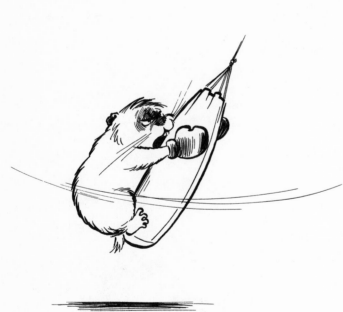

7

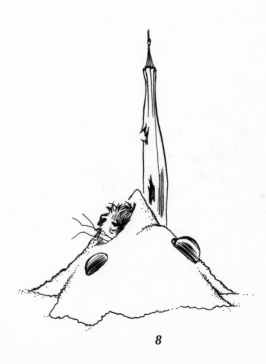

8

1

2

3

4

5

6

7

8

9

3

1

2

4

5

6

2

1

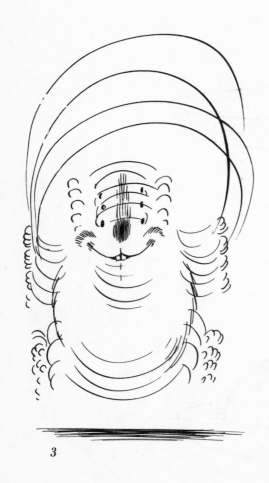

3

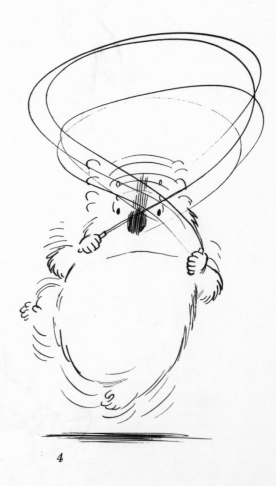

4

5

6

7

8

3

2

1

4

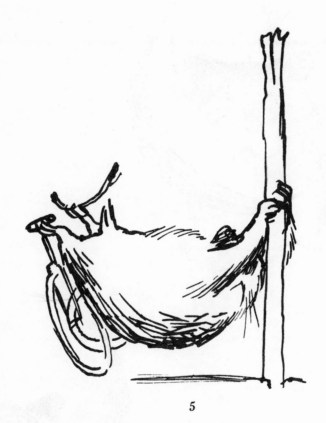

5

1

2

3

4

3

2

1

4

5

6

1

2

3

4

5

6

7

8

3

2

1

4

5

6

1

2

3

4

5

6

7

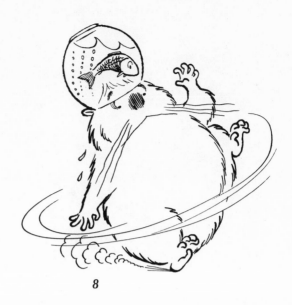

8

9

10

11

3

2

1

4

5

6

1

2

3

4

5

3

2

1

4

5

6

1

2

3

4

5

6

7

8

3

2

?

1

4

5

6

1

2

3

4

5

6

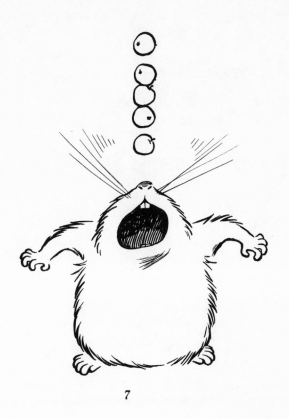

7

8

3

2

1

4

5

6

1

2

3

4

5

6

7

8

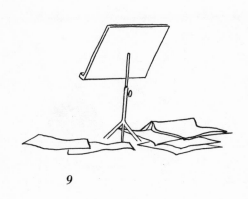

9

10

1

2

3

4

5

6

7

8

9

3

2

1

4

5

6

3

2

1

4

5

6

THE END

7